The Authorised Guide to

# GRUNTY FEN

### Gateway to the East

by

## Christopher South

*Edited by Carol Carman and typed by Miss Edwards
with illustrations by John Holder*

First published in 2014 by Grunty Fennery

ISBN: 978-0-9930130-0-3

An address for Grunty Fennery can be found
through the 'Contact Us' section of the website
http://www.dennisofgruntyfen.co.uk/shop/

Printed and bound in Great Britain by Book Printing UK
Remus House, Coltsfoot Drive, Peterborough, PE2 9BF

# Contents

# Contents

# LIST OF ILLUSTRATIONS

This book is dedicated to the memory of Pete Sayers

without whom it would have been impossible.

# ACKNOWLEDGEMENTS

The Author would like to thank
Miss Edwards, Carol Carman, Martin Carman and Janet South
whose ceaseless nagging, bullying and interference
made this book what it is.

# 1. INTRODUCTION

It would be foolish to suggest that the modest charms of Grunty
Fen could ever rival its near neighbours, Cambridge and Ely, as
tourist attractions. Grunty Fen will never rank with Florence or
even Diss as a cultural or historical venue. Yet it is true to say
that there is nowhere else on earth quite like it.

For almost 20 years I made a series of radio programmes
for the BBC based in Grunty Fen. Over that period, just as the
ducks struggle to break through the crust covering the village
pond, I managed to glimpse the truth beneath the surface.

The time has come to set down what I know and give
Grunty Fen this, its first guide book.

The people of Grunty Fen do not go out of their way to
charm strangers. Tempered by centuries of hardship, surviving
every sort of plague and pestilence from the green flux (*see
Health 4.2*) to sprout weevil, these stoical people may seem surly
but are unstinting in their generosity and, as I have witnessed
myself, would give their last dressed capon to a neighbour if he
was definitely hungry and never think of seeking any reward until
better times return.

These sturdy folk are proud of their achievements and
reluctant to make changes. Even when new technology is

accepted, it is in a hesitant and haphazard fashion. The pencil sharpener, for example, arrived fully ten years before the pencil. More calamitously, the tea cosy arrived almost twenty years before the tea pot and was widely believed to be some sort of family planning apparatus, as census figures for that period all too clearly show. Yet it cannot be denied the eventual acceptance of the bicycle brought a dramatic improvement to the human gene pool.

Early records are scanty. The pipe roll archives of Ely Cathedral allude to a Gruntye or Gungy Fenne in the 12th century in a context which has led to speculation that the community began as some sort of penal colony for erring brothers. Indeed, there still survives on the southern edge of the parish a boggy tangle of thorn and thistle called Monks' Bushes. One elderly resident in the 1980s claimed on his death-bed that he alone knew the secret of what the monks did in the bushes. Alas, he then expired so we may never know what happened long ago in that ancient thicket although speculation remains rife at The Bull Inn when ladies predominate on bingo nights.

Legend and speculation are the very stuff of Grunty Fen's earliest history. Ask how this flat landscape originated and they will mutter ominously: "The fen suck," reflecting a widespread belief that this was once a hilly region. Legends of lost villages are widespread – Gnashing, Drear and Meazly among others were all supposedly "sucked" into the fen. Although archaeologists and geologists pour scorn on these old stories, it has to be said that an otherwise inexplicable gurgling noise sometimes emanates from the plughole in St Judas' Church font which clergy and congregation will insist is connected to no known drainage system.

Proud of their heritage, the people of Grunty Fen display little sense of historical progression. What are called "the olden days" cover all eras from "before the railway came" extending back into pre-history when, according to another popular belief, an extensive forest of gigantic rhubarb covered the entire area from the coast almost as far as Cambridge, browsed by herds of dinosaurs. These magnificent beasts finally died out because they

were unable to extract sufficient nutriment from their diet as the rhubarb made its rapid passage through their digestive system. This supposedly accounts for the rich black fen soil but not for the demise of the forest of which, according to local belief, the sole remaining evidence is the wrongly named bog oaks which are in fact petrified rhubarb.

Fanciful or not, rhubarb still plays a central role in fen life, notably in a system of semaphore signalling (see *Communications 4.6*) and formerly in industry (see *Industry 4.1*).

# 2. CAUTIONARY NOTES

## 2.1 Earth Movement

While the greatest care has been taken in giving details of the location and orientation of sites of topographical interest, the reader should not assume that anything will be found exactly as this guide says in terms of location or orientation.

Not only does the ever-shifting surface of the fen alter natural features (Hell Knoll, for example, is now a hole but may well be a knoll again one day) but the direction of flow of ditches and dykes may reverse.

For entirely different reasons supposedly fixed boundaries may vary subtly from year to year. This is due to the time-honoured custom of appropriating land from a neighbouring plot.

In the absence of the owner of a plot, his neighbour may move a fence, even a living hedge, to gain a few inches. Gradually, over a period of years, a garden may double in size and there are celebrated cases where the owner of land is encroached on one side but is himself encroaching on the other so that a whole field has been known to move several hundred yards.

This is not only a cartographer's nightmare but it explains why Grunty Fen landowners are so reluctant to go on holiday without leaving a family member to guard all frontiers.

## 2.2    *Feral Nuns*

The most bloodcurdling accounts of attacks by the so-called
"**Feral Nuns**" can be discounted.

It is most improbable, for example, that a lone bus driver
returning to his depot at midnight was kidnapped crossing Bleak
Fen and vanished until he was found ten years later appearing as
"The Amazing Quivering Man" in a freak show at Great
Yarmouth.

Similar stories proliferate and are believed without
question by local people; pastors in chapels of every creed
incorporate prayers to keep their flocks safe from the nuns.

However, there is some documentary evidence that an
order of sisters defied excommunication by the Pope in 1479 and
fled to the remotest wildernesses of the still undrained fens,
leading a nomadic existence between islands of reeds and raiding
small settlements of eel trappers.

Later chronicles develop the theme of men being carried
away by the "Little Sisters of Perpetual Availability".  Such
reports abound in the present day when marauding raiding parties
of nuns are said to go about on fleets of Vespa motor scooters.
With this in mind, a male visitor to Grunty Fen and the entire area
should consider avoiding going out alone in the hours of darkness

and, if this cannot be avoided, taking several women with him for protection.

# 3.  THE PLACE

## 3.1    Architecture

### 3.1.1   Architectural Epochs

The history of architecture in the Grunty Fen area can broadly be divided into three periods, starting with **The Perpendicular Period (c.1850-1920)** which is characterised by the use of corrugated iron sheeting on a wooden frame or sometimes self-supporting but invariably secured so that the corrugations are vertical or inclined in the vertical plane. A typical example is the Chapel of the Doomed Brethren at Pious End.

**The Horizontal Period (c.1920-1940)** arose when the great period of Perpendicular construction was largely completed and it only remained to create pig sties and similar stock enclosures when it would have been wasteful to erect barriers six feet or more in height.

It is a principle of both styles of architecture that a sheet must never be cut since this would reduce its versatility, limiting its usefulness in future and so severely diminishing its value. Buildings may come and go but "**the galvanised**", as the corrugated sheets are called, lives on for ever. Some sheets have served a term in as many as six structures and each is identifiable not only to its owner but to most other villagers.

The single exception to the rule against altering a sheet of galvanised is the making of a corner. This is a great skill and involving bending a sheet at right angles across the corrugations in a straight line and without puncturing the metal. Some superb examples of this can be seen in the Village Hall kitchen lean-to.

What might be called the third, the **Baroque** or **Curvilinear Period** dates from the Second World War when curved sheets of heavy corrugated steel became available for air raid shelters and self-supporting military buildings such as Nissen huts. This triggered a revolution in Grunty Fen architecture.

 Suddenly, elegant, streamlined pig sties and goat sheds sprang up across the fen and an entire Nissen hut was commandeered by a religious sect led by the religious visionary Scaly Salmon (see *Religion 4.3*).

Second only to galvanised as a vital component in the development of Grunty Fen architecture is the railway sleeper. So precious are these creosoted baulks of timber that they are still widely used in bartering (see *Currency 4.7*).

But as a building material they serve every purpose from flooring to walls with the exception of roofing which is ruled out by their weight.  Some of the finest sleeper buildings are the Damnation Chapels built for the Salvation of the Lost and Perplexed at many isolated crossroads on the fen.

### 3.1.2   *St Judas' Church*

The church itself is a building of indeterminate age and in a rich range of materials including Formica, clunch, stone, brick, asbestos and corrugated iron.

The brief popularity of fire worship in the late 19th century means that little remains of the original wooden structure of St Judas'.  The ground-plan of the present structure, with its various lean-to's, sheds and subsidiary chapels, takes the approximate form of a mandala or swastika.

Sadly the **tower**, which dates from the early 20$^{th}$ century, finally fell into disuse when its asbestos sheeting was condemned by the Health and Safety Executive.  Subsidence had long made it impossible to ring the bells which were sold for scrap to pay the then vicar's expenses in a long legal dispute with the British Naturist Union.

Perhaps the most striking feature of the church is the **chancel**, the apsoidal design of which was clearly influenced by the widespread use of WWII Army Nissen huts at the time of its construction.  Indeed, it may actually be, in whole or part, a

Nissen hut although ingeniously pierced by lancet windows glazed with colourful sections cut from former shop window displays whose origin is scarcely detectable until, for a small gratuity, the verger (who introduces himself as Dennis) points out to the visitor's astonishment that the Virgin was once the Ovaltine girl, Saints Peter and Paul were the Bisto Kids and the Feeding of the Five Thousand is contrived from an advertisement for Nut Brown Shag.

One of St Judas' few strictly antiquarian glories is a **brass**, set into the floor of what at the time of writing is the South East aisle (St Judas' changes alignment from time to time due to subsidence). This elegant medieval work depicts a knight in full armour although the zealous use of Brasso and Duraglit by the devoted ladies of the congregation has long since obliterated the family name of the deceased nobleman. For a small gratuity the verger will explain that the brass is known and respected by all as "Sir Hugo de Wosname" – a corruption of "What's-his-name". For a further small fee the verger discloses that Sir Hugo has become the object of a minor local fertility cult in which childless women sacrifice small rodents on the pet dog or possibly ferret depicted at the knight's feet. Sadly, the resulting smears and tiny giblets make this ancient masterpiece even more indecipherable.

The church does possess one other unique treasure, an

imposing lectern **Bible** incorporating between the First and Second Books of Samuel a further book encountered in no other holy work, the **Book of Ezeriah**. Biblical scholars cannot fathom how or where Ezeriah originated or from which tongue it came to be translated into English, but the work is held in high esteem by the people of Grunty Fen, many of whom refer to it almost daily for guidance.

One passage from Chapter XIV, vv 13-27 is widely committed to memory for readily available comfort and solutions to life's problems. It begins: *"Lo even he who has and having had hath not had all such as those who hath not had nor even hath not had less than that which those who hath had, let them yet have even as much as these others who say, 'We had and hath not' for they hath not had so much as he who says, 'I have and shall have all that is we had and yet have it not'."* Many local men would not consider completing a football pools coupon or proposing marriage without first consulting the wisdom of Ezeriah.

The **organ**, which can only be used outside the owl-nesting season, has most standard hymns in its range but, for a small gratuity, the verger will demonstrate how it also plays "Let's All Go Down The Strand" and "I Love a Lassie". For a small additional gratuity he will perform a karaoke version of "The Laughing Policeman".

*Miss Edwards from Grunty Fen Post Office Stores is a virtuoso on the mighty organ of St Judas'. She is happy to oblige not just on Sundays but on any day of the week (retail duties permitting). In order to reach full throttle her organ needs constant manual pumping by the verger, Dennis.*

### 3.1.3  *Village Hall*

After St Judas', the **Village Hall** (see *Social Life 4.4*) is perhaps the most remarkable building in the parish incorporating Perpendicular, Horizontal and Curvilinear galvanised together with a very wide variety of other materials including polyvinylchlorate and expanded polystyrene crockets.

The hall's exterior often puzzles visitors who cannot understand why it has several elaborate porches which do not lead to entrances and several entrances which have no porches. This is accounted for by the slow but ceaseless and irregular movement to and fro and up and down of the site on which the hall was built.

Approaches to the hall are generally on more solid ground where it is convenient to erect a porch. Thus, as the hall swivels slowly one way or another its entrances leave its porches behind and new porches may have to be built to serve the repositioned doorway.

The Committee have considered a plan to re-build the hall in a circular form set within a stationary circular verandah so that access could be gained from any direction by drawbridge but the expense has so far made this impossible.

### 3.1.4   The LNER

One of the most attractive examples of local architecture owes its existence, like the sleepers, to the railway.  Several families have lived in converted Victorian and Edwardian railway carriages for generations.  Dennis, who was so helpful in research for this guide, was born in and still lives in just such a carriage – known as **The LNER** – with his 92-year-old grandmother.  Her bedroom was once the $1^{st}$ Class compartment and still has the string luggage racks and framed panoramic views of seaside resorts dating from when it plied the lines of the London & North Eastern Railway.  Other compartments are allocated to parlour, scullery and a seldom used space at one end reserved for entertaining guests on important occasions furnished with an impressive radiogram which, since the carriage lacks electricity, is used to store coal and kindling.

Among the many sheds surrounding The LNER is a unique structure measuring some 20ft x 10ft and of which the

---

*Left: The author and Dennis outside The LNER.  Note the old Wolseley car used as a hen coop, and through the window in the door of the Third Class Compartment Gran is about to hand Dennis a mug of tea.  To the right of the picture is a corner of the Miscellaneous Shed and in the background can be seen the majestic Ship of The Fens, Ely Cathedral.*

walls are made entirely of old interior and exterior doors.  This is
the **Miscellaneous Shed** and the use of doors on all sides is
intended to confuse any thief seeking to get in.  Only one door
works but it is undistinguishable from all the others.


### 3.1.5  *Pill Boxes*

Another architectural heritage from the Second World War
is the presence of several surviving concrete defensive structures

*Bulk of Spam here*

or "**pill boxes**" which now make snug first-
time homes for young couples.  A few pill
boxes in remote areas whose exact location is
a closely guarded secret, still contain stocks of wartime supplies
(see *Cuisine 4.8*).


### 3.1.6  *Oddities*

Finally we must mention the most numerous class of
dwellings which fall into none of the formal categories so far
mentioned but have simply accreted over the years from **found
materials**.

The shape and design is dictated by the shape and
dimensions of the window frames, doors, etc. found at refuse
disposal sites or in skips, or occasionally whole wall panels which
have been blown off passing building materials lorries by the

fierce fen winds.

Much of the more flamboyant exterior and interior decorations come from the misshapes scrap heap at "The Extrusions," the nearby plastics factory. Note the fluorescent orange cherubs on No.7, The Council Houses.

Not strictly architectural but notable nonetheless are the unique **greenhouses** and **cloches** in use at allotments and private gardens. These are made from the rear gun turrets, pilots' canopies and flight deck windows of WWII and later military aircraft. These vestiges of Blenheims and Lancasters now protect lettuces and tomatoes. Nor has the supply dried up. Many glazed segments of current bombers and fighters incautiously left unattended at the nearby Mildenhall and Lakenheath USAF bases may be seen doing service as conservatories as well as greenhouses.

A striking feature of local architecture are the famous **leaning houses**. Most private houses and bungalows start to lean one way or the other shortly after completion. No attempt is made to rectify even the most extreme tilt because it is accepted that the building will sooner or later, given the unpredictable nature of the fen soil, start to tilt another way.

Woollie Woodlands Sloping House

For this reason all houses are fitted with extra brackets and pegs so that sloping shelves can be swivelled.  Fen furniture makers have invented chairs and tables with adjustable legs and strong ceiling hooks are provided so that most domestic appliances can be suspended when the floods come in the rainy season between June and April.

Visitors are sometimes amused when their attention is proudly directed to "the highest man-made structure in the village" but it is true that since recent subsidence the tower of St Judas' is now several feet shorter than the gents' **stink pipe** at **The Bull Inn.**

Perhaps more surprisingly, the stink pipe has two serious purposes for the entire community apart from the obvious one. First, it is ideal for flying the Union Jack on great occasions such as a royal Jubilee or wedding and faded fragments of flags can be seen still dangling from the top since the Coronation and, more recently, Her Majesty's success at Ascot in 2013.

More practically, the stink pipe is used to measure journeys, so **Foul Fen** is described as "four miles from the stink pipe" and strangers may be asked how far from the stink pipe they originate. Be ready with a good reply!

# Hitler's Hole

One of the most interesting sights for tourists is **Hitler's Hole**, a supposedly bottomless pit opened up by a Luftwaffe bomb in 1942.

For generations this unique asset has served as an emergency dump during a police swoop. In its time the hole is said to have consumed an entire USAF armoured personnel carrier in one gulp and thousands of gallons of illicit alcohol.

The hole is seldom used for ordinary domestic garbage because of an extreme reluctance to throw anything away. For this reason there is no local refuse disposal service.

## 3.2    Flora, Fauna and Weather Lore

### 3.2.1    Flora

This is but a brief guide to the many pretty wild plants unique to Grunty Fen:

**Bastard Lashweed** (*Causticus Emetica*):   Admired chiefly for the ulcer-like bodies formed along its curiously tough tendrils which extend to over a yard and can snare the ankles of passers-by.  Once their prey is thus held the ulcers exude a toxic glue.  Also known as Witches' Shins.

**Evil Graspwort** (*Agonia Diabolica*):   This pretty hedgerow plant is covered in graceful, pendulous hair-like stings which when brushed, become erect and administer a lethal toxic dose of a chemical resembling curare.  Harvested and dried, it was used in the 13th and 14th centuries to treat fistula in mules but is today employed solely to stuff the pillows of chronic insomniacs.

**Sick Child** (*Infanta Vomica*):   The country name for this handsome herb springs from the remarkable resemblance the small green flower bears to the face of a child suffering from a nasty gastric attack.  Its noxious reputation is, however, greatly exaggerated. Only mildly poisonous, Sick Child is seldom entirely fatal, producing spasms of acute stomach cramps which cause some discomfort but pass off in a day or two. It is a vital constituent in country brides' bouquets.

**Beggar's Brat Curdle** (*Infanta Mendicantius*): This attractive wayside herb with its spiked black leaves and small thorny black flowers was long believed to help female tramps feed their young but is now used to make a cheap polish for cycle lamps and other chromium appliances. Dried bunches of Beggar's Brat Curdle are still used in some remote fen villages to dust ivory piano keys.

**Pauper's Death Rattle** (*Spikea Tintinnabulis Mortuary*): This attractive plant whose large black berries ooze purple mucus in late autumn, is chiefly known for its long, dry fronds. It is these which give Pauper's Death Rattle its quaint folk name. The slightest breeze sets the fronds brushing against one another making a sound said to be exactly like that of a dying tramp.

### 3.2.2   *Fauna*

**Rats** (*Ratus ratus*): Prevalent throughout.

### 3.2.3   Old Gerkin's Weather Lore

Cast not a vest when the wind is in the West

Wear extra cloth when the wind is in the North

Cover up your mouth when the wind is in the South

And when the wind is in the East you can roll your sleeves up,

Unless it's February.

~ ~ • ~ ~

When shop windows glisten with chill, icy glaze

 And icicles hang in retail displays

And all this happens on warm, sunny days

 You know they've been out with their aerosol sprays.

~ ~ • ~ ~

When rain do swamp the farm and fen

And mud befouls the old A10

'Tis time to harvest beet again.

~ ~ • ~ ~

# 4.  THE PEOPLE

## 4.1.  Industry

### 4.1.1  Extrusions and Fancies

Very few residents of the area are employed in any visible commercial enterprise yet even fewer are registered unemployed and no-one appears ill-fed, ill-shod or shabby.  Official statistics are scanty and totally unreliable since they are concerned solely with those people whose births have been registered.

None can doubt the total loyalty of everyone to Queen and country.  Devotion to Her Majesty is quite ferocious.  Yet there is a widespread reluctance to take up conventional citizenship.

For these reasons, few people living in the immediate vicinity are employed in formal local industrial enterprises, notably a factory producing plastic mouldings known as "**The Extrusions**", and a patisserie bakery known as "**The Fancies**". All workers at these plants are bussed in from distant areas like Pious End, Great Guttering and Rat Dyke with large numbers of registered inhabitants.  Yet those living close by benefit enormously from these two factories.  Misshapen fancy cakes, reject tarts and empty cream horns have long been a staple part of the Grunty Fen diet and faulty horns are at the heart of Grunty Fen

WI social calendar (see *Societies 4.5*). Similarly, misshapen extrusions are an important element in local house construction (see *Architecture 3.1*).

### *4.1.2   Carrots and Offal*

Because of their more relaxed attitude to National Insurance, Health & Safety and the Inland Revenue, two industries do attract numbers of Grunty Fen workers. They are the **Carrot Scrubbing Sheds** and the **Offal Sheds** in the neighbouring village of Windy Huts, which enjoys a reputation much worse than the crime figures actually show. Females are the principal workers in both cases.

In the Carrot Sheds scores of girls scrub carrots before they are packed for market and in the Offal Sheds even greater numbers of girls strip the carcasses of fallen or diseased farm livestock to secure those parts which retain some value as tallow, horticultural blood, pet food or for the oriental pharmaceutical trade. It has been truly said that if a Grunty Fen girl has a job she is either a scrubber or a stripper.

# BEAUTY
## in Grunty Fen

*Work in the Carrot Scrubbing Sheds may sound unglamorous but for some it is a land of opportunity promising fame and wealth. The girls themselves attribute their radiant complexion to the aerosol-like fine mist of moist carrot debris saturating the atmosphere of the scrubbing sheds. Whatever the explanation, their faces glow with a sort of healthy jaundice which is the envy of their friends who labour in the Offal Sheds.*

*Dulcie Vetch is the most successful beauty of recent years. Dulcie won the title of "Miss Scrubber" in 2004 and went on to bear the coveted title of "Miss Bedding Stuff", awarded each spring by local nurserymen and garden centres. Dulcie never returned to the carrot sheds and now owns a shed of her own on the road between Stark and Guttering where she runs a beauty salon under the name Dolores Allure. Her partner, Clint, rents her lean-to for his unisex hairdressers, Shock Treatment. OAPs half-price Tuesdays.*

### 4.1.3   Rhubarb

The Golden Age in Grunty Fen's industrial history bloomed and faded with the British Empire. The gaunt remains of the **Imperial Rhubarb Mills** still stand on a bleak and solitary fen that was once thick with rhubarb fields to the horizon. In season the great steam-powered mill worked 24 hours a day producing slab rhubarb. Before the days of canned rhubarb colonial pioneers in Her Majesty's far-flung realm longed for the vegetable which, in a popular song of the time, "Keeps the Regular Army Regular."

It was a fen farmer, Enderby Grizewood, who seized this opportunity and set up a modest factory for stewing, desiccating and pressing large "ingots" of rhubarb for export. Within a decade a constant convoy of narrow boats laden with slabs of rhubarb carried Grizewood's products to seagoing vessels at King's Lynn and thence to the furthest corners of the earth. Its imperishable quality meant it could be stored anywhere from bungalow larders to quartermasters' stores for ready availability in war or peace. The relief of Lucknow, Mafeking and many other reliefs can in part be ascribed to Grizewood's genius.

It is not perhaps altogether fanciful to attribute the decline of the British Empire to an event at the Grizewood slab factory on May 17 1904. Keen to build on his first success, Grizewood had invested in a second factory to produce **custard**. On that fell day the pressure vessels in the custard hall blew up in a violent explosion that ruined the neighbouring rhubarb factory and scattered immense blobs of custard over a very wide area. Dykes and ditches became clogged with custard and partially rehydrated rhubarb. Armed with galvanised buckets, townspeople from as far away as Cambridge came in a sort of custard Klondike to gather what they could and for weeks afterwards famished infants in the poorer streets grew plump on food that had, like manna, dropped from heaven.

For details of guided tours of the rhubarb and custard works ruins, enquire at the Post Office.

**Daniel Lubbock**

**Sept 6<sup>th</sup> 1889**

**–**

**May 17<sup>th</sup> 1904**

**Blowed Up**

*Visitors to the St Judas' churchyard are often puzzled to find among the tilting gravestones one bearing this enigmatic epitaph (left).*

*Miraculously, Daniel, who died aged 24 leaving a widow and eleven children, was the only fatal victim of the Great Custard Disaster. He had been sleeping on a heap of slab rhubarb beside the custard boilers when the works exploded.*

*A relief fund set up for his widow still continues its work among the poor of the parish and last year provided a treat for the Over 60s-Club in a ceremony at which a tube of wine gums was blessed by the vicar before distribution.*

### 4.1.4  Agriculture and Slurry

No panorama of Grunty Fen industry would be complete without exploring a single activity which is at once the smallest and the largest – **agriculture**. Highly mechanised, the farms employ very few workers but are the most profitable industry by far. Now entirely arable, here and there vast **slurry lagoons** remain as reminders of a once thriving dairy industry and flocks of sheep once grazed these fields of roots and grains. The slurry lagoons still serve as play places of happy youngsters.

Those few who still work the land for the farmers are possibly the last survivors in Europe of the centuries-old system of serfdom. Considered the elite of the local labouring class, they have food, clothing and shelter for life and are envied by all for their good fortune. Farmers see it as part of their pastoral duties to oversee a religious sect, the **Earthly Paradise Church**, whose creed matches the needs of the bonded workers (see *Religion 4.3*).

# *FERVOUR*
## *in Grunty Fen*

*Patriotic fervour occasionally causes an individual to emerge from the obscurity of the unregistered and declare an intention to fight for his country but the outcome is seldom a happy one.*

*Dennis, the Verger at St Judas' who has been such a help in researching these pages, tells how as a young man he volunteered to do his National Service in the Army. Lacking any official papers, he turned up at Bassingbourn Barracks proudly bearing as a gesture of his enthusiasm a live WWII hand grenade he had found in a former Home Guard concrete pill-box on Sludge Fen. To his dismay, he was turned away. "Soon as I showed them that grenade they snatched it off me and couldn't wait to get rid of me."*

*This incident illustrates the Grunty Fenner's confident cast of mind. He was convinced that by arriving with a grenade he would be doing the Army a favour and points out that had they been more welcoming he would have let the Army have his large stock of 303 rifle ammunition.*

## 4.1.5   *Plunder Truck*

The largest part of the Grunty Fen economy is not only invisible but regrettably illegal.  Local people fall silent or change the subject at any mention of "**plunder truck**" yet it has been a principal component of trade for generations.  The police, revenue and other branches of government know it happens but seem powerless to act.

In short, at night and in difficult weather conditions when visibility is poor, **plundermen** use false lights and diversion boards to lure huge articulated lorries and container trucks off the A10 and down narrow fen lanes from which it is almost impossible for the innocent driver to escape.  When the poor wretch leaves his cab and wanders off to seek aid, the plundermen swoop and ransack his load.  Long before dawn the entire contents of a mighty truck or container have been whisked away in a dozen different directions and hidden.

Apart from the disgracefully dishonest nature of this practice, it also creates a curiously unpredictable element in the fen economy which has suddenly to digest several thousand Chinese lanterns, novelty chopsticks and catering packs of prawn crackers, or 24 gross of surgical boots, scores of bridal head-dresses, assorted anchovy snacks, 2000 aubergines, nylon mufflers and 100 side drums.  In time such heterogeneous hauls find homes but some take longer than others.

Sometimes on warm days with a slight breeze from the west visitors can still sniff traces of the 300 drums of liniment taken by the plundermen one foggy night in 1958. Almost all mechanical parts, from the sliding doors at the carrot sheds to the crank that raises and lowers the stage curtain at the Village Hall are lubricated with the huge quantity of condemned industrial salad cream taken in 1982. The same salad cream is used to waterproof boots and soothe chafed hands. It is even sometimes used on salads but only sparingly after what happened at the gala tug of war in 2002.

## 4.2    Health

Grunty Fen boasts both an experienced general practitioner in **Dr Wallace** and a bustling **Cottage Hospital**.

After 30 years as a doctor in the Merchant Navy, Dr Wallace says nothing his patients do can surprise him, not even in Grunty Fen. His consulting room has all the usual medical equipment together with a sulphur-crested cockatoo called Nursey whose words are given great weight. During an examination of a patient the bird may remark "That's a big-un!" or "It's me nerves" so perceptively that villagers have come to trust Nursey more than the doctor himself and the receptionist is often asked to book a diagnostic session with the sagacious cockatoo.

The Cottage Hospital, which is loosely affiliated to the NHS, offers a wide range of services although its strictly medical functions are limited. Most local people hire the ambulance at very competitive prices for light removals and it can be decked out with white ribbons for weddings if it has not already been allocated for seaside excursions in the holiday season.

Weekend breaks with hospital bed and breakfast are popular with free access to the Bedside Manor Country House spa and sluice room. Further details from Matron. All major cards accepted.

Not quite so popular as Lourdes, Grunty Fen is also a place of **pilgrimage** for hundreds of chesty people from many miles away every November 5th when they stand downwind of the bonfire and breathe deeply. Although the fuel of the fire varies from year to year it is largely used to dispose of those items taken from "lost" lorries (see *Industry 4.1*) which proved no use or value.

A tank of condemned industrial marzipan is always added to get the blaze going and this creates vast clouds of highly therapeutic smoke.

---

**Warning:** *Visitors to Grunty Fen should beware the green flux, the disease which has plagued the community since medieval times.*

*Since there is no treatment for the green flux, health experts advise visitors not to touch anything or eat anything during the season when the flux is most virulent – between March and January.*

*However, an application of Mother Margery's Patent Poultice, available at the Post Office, is a herbal remedy widely trusted. Boiled and served with custard the poultices are also a popular pudding.*

## 4.3    Religion

The practice of religion is a complex and ever-changing scene in the Grunty Fen area.  For up-to-date information about the multitude of sects, sub-sects, persuasions and faiths available the visitor should enquire at the Post Office on the eve of the Sabbath for the latest information.

The only more-or-less settled place of worship is the parish church, St Judas', where the traditional Anglican liturgy is observed together with a range of animist and pagan alternatives in the side chapels and odd corners.

Religious history here is one of ceaseless change and the countryside for miles around is littered with the ruins of **chapels** which prospered briefly before falling into disuse, often because the predicted date of the end of the world failed to materialise.

Grunty Fen itself is remarkable in having somewhere between three and eight chapels, give or take, whereas the tiny neighbouring settlement of **Pious End**, which draws worshippers from far and wide on all holy days of the week, has many more chapels than inhabitants.

Most Pious End residents attend several chapels every day and at the great festivals (Easter, Christmas, Eelfest, Bloodmassnight, Doombind, Odin's Day, Slaughtering, The Coming and The Going), members of choirs may sing in a dozen different services so music lovers are advised to go to the earlier rather than later assemblies when the choirs grow hoarse.

The most remarkable survivor among this multiplicity of sects is **The Chapel of Light** which takes its name not from divine light but because it is built out over a constantly eroding dyke bank into which it always seems in danger of falling. It is saved from doing so by the light brethren's policy of allowing nothing heavy at the altar end which overhangs the water. Stout worshippers are discouraged and if they persist in attending are assigned pews at the back. Turnips, potatoes and swedes are banned from Harvest Festival displays which include nothing larger than a lettuce or heavier than a radish.

Equally puzzling is the name of **The Chapel of the Total Adherents** at **Rat Dyke**, so called not because they are singularly strict in abiding by the rules of their religion but because the pews were painted with a varnish that has never quite set. Their pastor assures them their reward will be a dry throne in Heaven.

Although it is not represented at Pious End, one of the most enduring sects is that devoted to fish and all marine life.

**The Jonahs** were founded by the Rev "Scaly" Salmon in the early 50s when ex-Army Nissen huts were freely available.

Each chapel is a black Nissen hut painted with eyes to look like a whale and worshippers are summoned to service by the sight of a jet of water emerging through a hole in the roof by means of a sacred stirrup pump. Inside, walls, floor, pews and congregation are constantly hosed down by the Piscator. The Jonahs have no other purpose than to raise money to maintain their chapels which are, for obvious reasons, always in a state of rust and decay. Jonah fund-raisers travel door-to-door selling sardine sandwiches with or without tomato.

Other sects which may or may not still be functioning or have been supplanted, include those dedicated to **St Eam**, believed to have been the inventor of traction engines, **The Worshipful Waltzers** who pray to Victor Sylvester and believe they can quickstep their way into paradise and **The Verminators** which is restricted to rat catchers and their families but of whose beliefs and practices nothing is known.

The most ambitious chapel ever erected in the area was **The Grunty Fen Temple Bastion of Eternal Strength and Perpetual Impregnable Citadel of Everlasting Endurance** which, shortly after the opening ceremony, fell down (see illustration opposite).

The ruins of The Grunty Fen Temple Bastion of Eternal Strength and Perpetual Impregnable Citadel of Everlasting Endurance remain in a ditch just south of Scant and are a place of pilgrimage for those seeking assurance in an ever-changing world.

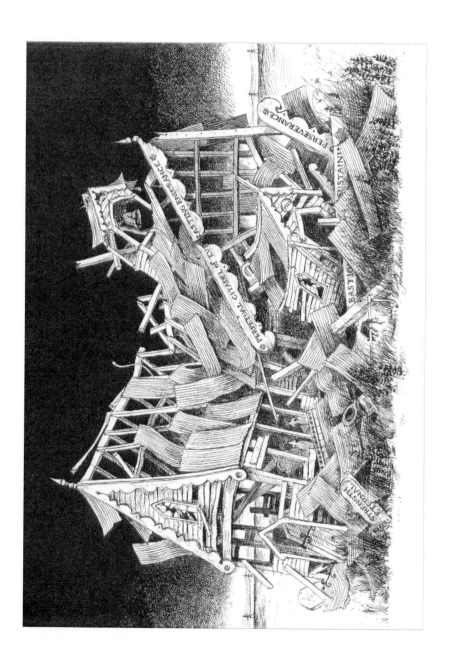

## 4.4    Social Life

### 4.4.1    The Arts

The hectic whirl of Grunty Fen's social life centres on the Village Hall though the state of the floor means numbers attending events have to be limited.  Dancers are advised to learn the weak spots before attempting anything more ambitious than the Veleta although, curiously enough, the wide strides demanded to ensure safe passage around the floor spectacularly enhance the performance of those dancing the Tango.

Sadly, one excellent village dancer, **Mrs Starling**, has had to be banned because of the damage caused not only to the floor but the walls.  Her vigorous version of flamenco was inspired by a week in Costa del Mar from which she returned with half a set of castanets, having lost the other in transit.  Compensating by banging her remaining castanet on the walls not only harmed the woodwork but caused such a serious fall of soot when she banged the stove chimney pipe that she ended up, according to the verger, "looking like a black and white minstrel."

The hall is also used for successful **stage entertainments** of which the most notable in recent years was a brilliant local adaptation of the great Broadway musical, "Singing in the Drain." The annual **pantomime** is notorious for the behind-the-scenes artistic tensions caused by the choice of which story to stage. Compromises have involved such productions as "Aladdin and his Wonderful Cat", "Babes in the Boots" and "Dick Hood and His Three Merry Bears."

Typical of the enthusiasm for the arts in Grunty Fen was when in a performance of **Handel's Messiah** the singers outnumbered the audience 35 to 1.

**The Grunty Fen Fine Arts Society** offers a varied range of speakers and courses. A recent season included "Decorating your dog", "Making the most of mash", "The stately bungalows of East Anglia" and "New ways with old buckets". This last talk reflects a strong local tradition among the ladies of using buckets rather than bags. From sturdy galvanised shopping buckets to dainty evening buckets trimmed with lace or studded with sparkling gems, no self-respecting Grunty Fen woman would be seen without her bucket. Young men often judge a girl by her bucket. A familiar sight in early spring is to see a young blade turning down the tops of his Wellington boots and turning his fancy to trim buckets.

Another vigorous aspect of the arts is **poetry**. Grunty Fen has two resident poets, Honey Brite (nee Norah Merchant) and Inigo Haycock, former holiday camp entertainers who now live in a charming Elizabethan-style asbestos bungalow and pen up to a hundred verses daily for the greetings card industry.

But perhaps the finest poet from the village was vicar's daughter Agatha Gotobed (1875-1921). Inspired by the sight of a simple villager doggedly determined to make his regular shopping journey in preparation for the weekend, she was moved to write one of her most touching works. This poem, *"In Time of Flood,"* is preserved in her collected oeuvre, *"The Song of the Dyke,"* (privately published 1915). The last three verses of that seminal opus are given opposite.

*Above: Even today, as in Agatha Gotobed's time, simple journeys are not always easy in Grunty Fen.*

*Rise up, ye sons of Fenland waters!*
*Rise up, ye damp and muddy daughters!*
*Heed the lessons nature taught us*
*When the tide hath oft time caught us.*

*Strain thine oars in steely rowlocks!*
*Strain thine clinker-builded bulwarks!*
*Thou art thine captain, thou art thine cox*
*Though leaking boots make soggy socks*

*Naught shall dampen Tiger ardour*
*Clad in macintosh for armour*
*Row to Ely's welcome harbour*
*There at last to see thy barber*

When Miss Gotobed passed away, this verse was found
unfinished in her lifeless hand:

*Fare forward, Fenfolk, o'er thy flat fields.*
*Reap what bounteous nature yields,*
*Even if it is but few thin eels...*

45

## 4.4.2 Shopping

Grunty Fen has only two retail outlets but together they amply supply the daily needs of most shoppers. **The Post Office** houses the local telephone exchange as well as an astonishing range of foods, cosmetics, hardware, and pharmaceutical and veterinary products, many of which, like the Dauntless Goat Drench, are of local manufacture.

**Potts' Garage**, famous for "Potts' Thick", sells almost anything from heavy engineering to hairgrips in the form of plastic butterflies.

---

### *Potts' Garage*

*The almost magical properties attributed to "Potts' Thick" petrol from the bottom of the tank is only one of the unique services offered by this garage. The inspection pit which, over the years, has filled up with every sort of waste fluid from sump oil to caustic soda is used to cure a very wide range of mechanical failures. Simply by immersing a lawn mower, a sewing machine, a bicycle or any mechanism for a day or two infallibly releases jammed parts. However, recent experience suggests it should not be used for piano accordions unless replacement bellows are readily available.*

---

There is a third retail source, **Mrs Hind**, who has sat beside a quiet stretch of road outside the village for more years than even she can remember with a bucket of small glass beads and declares that she will continue to do so until they are all gone. As a serious contribution to Grunty Fen's mercantile scene, Mrs Hind and her bucket may seem of little account unless the visitor happens to be in need of beads but many passers-by stop to chat even though her conversation is largely limited to beads.

We will consider travelling merchants after further exploring the principal retailer.

**Grunty Fen
Post Office Stores**
*"Sink Tidies for all occasions"*

**Miss Edwards** and her reticent sister **Miss Edna** inherited the Post Office Stores from their father and have proudly sustained his standards with the single exception of their mobile grocery van which they had to abandon after it became impossible to keep apart the vast range of loose foodstuffs for which they remain famous.

Only after many years driving along bumpy roads while endeavouring to stop rice, humbugs, macaroni, porridge oats, caraway seeds, peanuts, cow cake, budgerigar millet and other comestibles becoming inextricably mixed with corn plasters, tap washers, nails, screws, roofing cleats, dog collars and veterinary powders did these redoubtable ladies give in. When finally clearing the van of its stores they bagged up the heterogeneous sweepings reeking of paraffin and still sell them as **novelty mystery dips**, popular with customers who enjoy sorting out the contents on long, dark evenings.

Equally tantalising for customers who enjoy taking a chance are the **bargain canned goods** from which the labels have washed off in the incurably damp store shed behind the shop. Some purchasers of these mystery tins claim that they can tell merely by shaking them and listening before purchase whether they contain, say, Irish stew or cling peaches in heavy syrup, although the wise housewife takes the precaution of opening the can before she promises her husband pilchards for supper and has to disappoint him with grapefruit segments.

The rest of the shop's stock is more orthodox and closely matches the everyday needs of a fen community. Rat traps and hurricane lamps dangle from the rafters alongside enema pumps and bicycle inner tubes. No attempt is made to categorise the stock generally because Miss Edwards firmly believes that it is only when a customer looking for an umbrella notices a display of cow licks that the idea of buying a lick crosses their mind.

Astute retailer though she is, Miss Edwards has over the years acquired quantities of such items as the 500 enamel sink tidies together with 2,000 aluminium thimbles, 17 gross of patent tie racks and a hundredweight of industrial dubbin when she falls prey to an equally astute young salesman she much admires. Miss Edwards freely admits that one whiff of his Silvikrin pomade and she loses her usual judgement.

The Edwards' shop is noted for its **spectacular window display**, a glittering mountain of glacier mints which has occupied the same space ever since the boiled sweets congealed together during a warm damp spell in the 1960s and have remained immoveable ever since.

Let us now turn our attention to a few of the itinerant merchants who pass through Grunty Fen.

### *The Lino Man*

*Visitors may catch a glimpse of one of the area's most unusual and elusive vendors – the Lino Offcuts Man. His van visits only sporadically but creates a great stir among those interested in interior decoration. Packed into the van are hundreds of pieces of linoleum left over from flooring contracts in more prosperous areas.*

*Potential purchasers jostle as the van doors open and they surge forward to seek out an off-cut that exactly fits the floor-space they wish to fill. An L-shaped offcut that will go from the front door, up the hall, round a left-hand corner and reach the kitchen, or even a T-shaped piece that will go to both the kitchen one way and a bedroom the other is rare and much sought after. Triangles, circles and the smaller squares are generally cheaper. If a piece of luxury lino becomes available, purchasers have been known to alter their houses to fit the shape of the lino.*

### Oily Olly

*Look out for Oily Olly, the mobile fish and chip man whose wrapping papers provide Grunty Fen with its main source of news from the outside world (see Communications 4.6).*

*He is notorious for braking his van too hard and slopping his hot fat in the village pond which has developed an iridescent crust impenetrable to ducks. Also, look out for Roy Beveridge, the mobile butcher in his van emblazoned with the proud boast "We don't sell no tripe."*

### Vinegar Potts

*Older fen people remember Vinegar Potts, grandfather of the current Potts' Garage owner.*

*He was an imaginative inventor and unique itinerant trader who believed he had spotted an opportunity when he saw the success of daily milk deliveries. Mr Potts started a daily vinegar round which flourished for less than a fortnight before housewives had sufficient stocks of vinegar not only as part of the daily diet but to clean their windows once a week for several years.*

### The Froth Man

*Like Mr Whippy in wealthier areas, the Froth Man is a central figure in any Grunty Fen childhood. Despite repeated attempts by health authorities to banish him and his bucket of froth, such is his popularity that he continues to make illicit forays on weekend afternoons shouting his wares "Froth! Froth! Froth!" through a megaphone he made from a small plastic bollard.*

*As if charmed by the Pied Piper, laughing, eager kiddies leave the slurry lagoons and run from all directions eager to pay a penny for a portion of the grey, tasteless foam in his bucket until it is all gone. As each spoonful is scooped into the palm of an outstretched hand the art is to suck up the froth before it blows away in the wind, Big boys tease the girls by blowing the froth from their hands as they raise it to their lips. Other boys engage in froth fights while the girls create fairy castles with theirs.*

*Although the health authorities have banned the sale of the grey froth on sanitary grounds, scientists have been unable to analyse what it is because it vanishes before they can get a sample to the laboratory.*

Left: a bookmark showing some of Grunty Fen's leading tradespeople.

(Note: Miss Edwards has asked me to say that this bookmark is available to buy through Dennis of Grunty Fen's website www.dennisofgruntyfen.co.uk but it should also be noted that not all of the bookmarks are supplied with string. It just depends what she can get her hands on.)

### 4.4.3 Sports and Pastimes

The usual national sports of football and cricket are popular together with one activity found only in the immediate Grunty Fen area – **Competitive Drain Rodding**. For health reasons, drain rodding is, like skiing and dominoes, strictly a winter sport. It is particularly popular at the council houses where up to a dozen rodders stand beside open manholes in Council Road and thrust rods towards each of the twelve houses where referees time the arrival of each competitor's rod when it reaches the inspection eye beside each home. Considerable strength as well as skill is required and large sums are paid for competition carbon fibre rods although some veterans claim their trusted old rattan rods are superior both in style and speed. But the real test is how quickly competitors can couple new sections of rod while still thrusting. Crowds gather round each manhole urging on sweating rodders with cries of "Foul drain!", "Stick stuck!", or "Up yours!"

The rodders of the village of Dank are current holders of the coveted inter-village rodding trophy in the shape of a silver manhole cover with filigree to support a dozen roses.

**Village football** is more orthodox but remarkable for a player breeding programme pursued for over fifty years. One family in the village, the **Thrussells**, produces very fast but bandy-legged players who tend to let the ball spin between their knees when defending a free kick. The other family, the **Nockolds**, produce excellent knock-kneed defenders who suffer severe chafing when running at speed.

The club archive includes a photograph of a Nockold flanked by two Thrussells whose six legs together clearly spell the word "OXO". However the breeding programme is now producing a number of both Nockolds and Thrussells who can turn their straight legs to either attack or defence.

**The Knoll**, home of **Grunty Fen Academicals**, is so called because it lies on a sloping area with unusually good drainage. Unfortunately this means that it is impossible to see all four corner flags from any one vantage point on the pitch or touchline. Nor can one goalkeeper see the other. Visiting teams claim this gives Academicals an unfair advantage but the Grunty Fen players point out that their rivals at Foul Fen, for example, mark out their pitch in almost invisible aubergine lines after acquiring several hundred gallons of the paint at a knock-down price in a liquidation sale at a failed interior decoration firm in Bloat and the pitch at Little Harm, to take a further example, is concrete and has the dung of bullocks marking the centre spot.

### *Funding Football*

*Grunty Fen Academicals' finances are in excellent order thanks to a steady income from sales of the sediment from the team bath which is believed to have miraculous healing and horticultural properties.*

*Small packets of dried sediment from the footballers' post-match ablutions have changed hands for as much as £10 with competition fiercest for the potent end-of-season scrapings.*

*The extraordinary girth and length of leeks winning local horticultural classes are attributed to this bath scum.*

*Academicals are also sponsored by The Fancies Factory to the extent of £17 a season and as many macaroons as the team can eat.*

**Cricket** is also played on The Knoll and so suffers the same visibility problem which is exacerbated by the popularity among fielders of wearing camouflage jackets. The Grunty Fen XI, St Judas' CC, gets practical help from the church in the form of numbers from the hymns and anthems boards either side of the chancel doing duty on the cricket score board.

For a small gratuity the verger allows visitors into the score box where he demonstrates how his system makes it impossible for "Last Man" to be given a psalm or for a team to have scored Hymn 203.

Since its establishment more than 30 years ago, **Grunty Fen Tennis Club** has acquired a large membership and an imposing trophy cabinet but still lacks trophies or even a court upon which to play. It is the committee's intention to lay down at least one hard court and many lorry-loads of hardcore, hoggin, clinker and ash have been used to that end.

However, the proposed site, acquired after a family of gypsies who had lived there for generations was wiped out by an outbreak of the green flux, so far offers no firm footing for sport. Several hundreds of tons of rubble taken from abandoned chapels (see *Religion 4.3*) quickly vanished beneath the surface when spread on the site and subsequent loads of concrete sleepers recovered from a railway engineering depot went the same way.

Clinker and hardcore linger scarcely a day before subsiding beneath the quaking surface.

Fortunately the clubhouse, a sturdy former mobile mass x-ray unit kindly donated by the Cottage Hospital (see *Health 4.2*) is mounted on a timber raft and is generally easily accessible by means of a plank bridge.

Fundraising evenings are an important part of the social calendar (see *Social Life 4.4*) and visitors admire the trophy cabinet acquired when Scant Co-Op butchery department was closed down by the sanitary inspector.  Sadly, it will lack trophies until the club can start to play tennis but founder-president Miss Babs Springer remains optimistic.

# 4.5.  Societies

## 4.5.1  Local History Society

**Grunty Fen Local History Society** has for some years been engaged in an ambitious genealogical survey to discover exactly who is related to whom in the village and how.  Sadly this laudable if contentious endeavour has met with fierce resistance from families who have refused to complete a questionnaire and abuse those who have.

The records formerly kept at the Parish Church, have been of little use since so many pages were used during the war to make cigarettes and other pages from the $16^{th}$ and $17^{th}$ centuries were used by the **Ladies' Craft Guild** to make novelty lampshades.  The remaining pages are so badly stained, scorched, torn or used by the **Sunday School** for colouring-in that they are almost useless.

Another problem confronting the project is that of those mentioned in completed forms more than seems humanly possible claim direct descent from a famous high-scoring early $20^{th}$ century Grunty Fen Academicals' centre-forward Gabriel "Bad Boy" Goodenson who was not the first person in the village to own a bicycle but was the first to learn how to ride one.

In 1985 the History Society published its interim

genealogical findings in a pamphlet entitled "A Grey Area" but this has been outdated by recent work on the effect of the proximity of two USAF bases.

### 4.5.2    The Grunty Fen Travellers' Club

**The Travellers' Club** relies chiefly on its own members for a lively season of talks and outings.  A highlight in any programme is the annual walk to Stretham for a fish and chip supper.  Successful talks in recent years have been Miss Treecott's account of a childhood outing to the Forty-Foot Drain and Mr Tapswell's popular story of how a bus broke down between Down Market and Bottle Bank for almost two hours and what the passengers did to pass the time.

### 4.5.3    The Loyal & Ancient Order of Goats

One of the greatest honours for any Fenman who has achieved eminence in his profession is to be invited to become a Goat.  **The Loyal & Ancient Order of Goats**, motto "Fromage du Chevre," is a long-established friendly society whose chief activity now is holding a sumptuous annual dinner.  So popular is the event and so numerous the attendance that it has become increasingly difficult to find a venue able to cope with such a prestigious function.

The last time the Goats' dinner was held in Grunty Fen Village Hall it was so crowded that waitresses were unable to enter and were forced to hand in food through windows or holes in the walls where rotten planks had fortuitously fallen away.

Scores of villagers who had not been invited to the dinner ringed the hall to glean the Scotch eggs and ladles of blancmange which unavoidably slipped from waitresses' grasp as they reached through the broken planks. The situation was made worse by a strong wind which lifted slices of ham like roofing slates and sent them flying into a hawthorn hedge where waitresses and villagers competed to pluck meat from the thorns.

This unfortunate experience led to a change in policy and Goats' dinners are now held in several sittings but the Universal Supreme Arch Goat, Mr Len Smithers, a distinguished poultry masseur from Drench, has proposed al fresco picnics as the long-term solution so that all Goats can be united for the **Great Bleat**.

### 4.5.4   *Women's Institute*

The **Women's Institute** is at the heart of social and cultural life and famous for its catering (see *Cuisine 4.8*). No longer formally associated with the national organisation since police were called to a group meeting with Windy Huts and Barnard's Sheds branches a few years ago, the ladies remain loyal to its traditions and hope to re-affiliate once the convictions lapse. At a recent wine making demonstration they sang "Jerusalem" before, during and after the meeting and were still singing Blake's great anthem as they wended their way home across the fen.

Among the most popular WI activities are ferretting, self-tattooing, stain removal, lace-making, wrestling and flower arranging.  A recent report in The Grunter (see *Communications 4.6)* gives a vivid picture of a typically lively meeting.  In her acceptance speech the current president, Mrs Enid Jolly, said her main aim in her term of office would be to prevent another lemon curd surplus at all costs and the situation had certainly improved lately although chutney levels were a new cause for concern. Members reported an overproduction of sloe gin but were confident they could handle it.

In the same report, the Secretary, Mrs Willing, appealed to the member who last used the Institute concrete mixer to please return it.


*4.5.5   Youth Clubs*

An informal **Youth Club** meets each evening behind the **half-timbered bus shelter** (so called after most of it goes for kindling each winter) and has been remarkably trouble free since they

Bus Shelter

agreed to clean up their own mess after meetings.

**Grunty Fen Boy Scouts** meet in the gents in The Bull since they were banned from the Village Hall for holding an indoor camp fire sing-song. The troop operates along the same lines as Scouts the world over except that they use wire instead of rope for knotting exercises and use floral loose covers from sofas and armchairs to create camouflage tents.

## 4.6   Communications

It always comes as a surprise to visitors from a world of smartphones and the worldwide web that the main means of communication around Grunty Fen, where the people are often scattered widely over windy fields, is **shouting**. This is the traditional manner of addressing friends even when at close quarters.

However, when fieldworkers are far apart or the wind so strong that even the loudest shout could not be heard, local people still sometimes resort to **rhubarb semaphore**. Although each letter of the alphabet can be represented by holding leafy rhubarb stalks like flags in each hand and waving them at arm's length, messages are generally confined to a few short gestures avoiding the need to spell out familiar phrases letter by letter.

Thus, "I have my foot caught in barbed wire" or "Police!" or "It's twins!" can be conveyed with a few flicks of a leaf, sometimes in relays over immense distances.

Apart from among a few newcomers, the landline telephone system has never caught on. The **kiosk** beside the Post Office is used only in extreme emergencies, partly because if the Post Office is closed the potential caller must rouse Miss Edwards or her sister, Miss Edna, to get the pre-decimal coins needed to operate the mechanism.

There is a switchboard in the Post Office but its proximity to the bacon slicer has for some years limited its scope.

As for **printed communication**, the newspapers used by the mobile fish and chip merchant Oily Olly (see *Industry 4.1*) are the most popular way of keeping up to date with the wider world. More locally, the weekly newspaper, **The Bugle**, is a valuable if sometimes confusing source. Serving some 30 villages in the area, *The Bugle* is only one of several publications printed in the same works. This means that *The Bugle* sometimes includes stray pages from *The British Xylophonist* (incorporating *Modern Glockenspiel*) or *The Gas Gazette* or *Amateur Taxidermist and Bird Stuffer*. Most readers welcome this as a bonus.

Within Grunty Fen itself, the parish magazine, **The Grunter**, consists chiefly of corrections and apologies arising from the previous issue, and accusations of libel or threats of legal action. It is of purely parochial interest. The vicar, the **Rev Quintin Partridge**, has refused to contribute to his own parish magazine since an unfortunate misprint stating that he had intended to preach a sermon on women's tights. Even though the church was packed for the first time in his ministry, he remains adamant.

### The BBC

*At a still secret location hidden in a thicket of brambles and rank elders is one of the most remarkable survivors of the darkest days of the Second World War when the BBC feared a Nazi invasion would drive it from London.*

*Seeking to ensure continual broadcasts to the Empire, a miniature Broadcasting House resembling a wayside chapel of ease was erected in a location it was hoped even the Gestapo would not find. Looking like a massive railway signal box, the interior has rows of heavy levers, brass-mounted dials on mahogany panels and the names of far-flung outposts of Empire in gilded lettering. (See illustration opposite.)*

*For a small fee, my guide, Dennis, set the whole system humming and showed how a single lever could send an edition of "Have a Go" starring Wilfred Pickles or a speech by Prime Minister Churchill winging its way to Fiji, Canada or Swaziland. Other levers are still able to transmit "ITMA" to Bangalore, "Much Binding in the Marsh" to Hong Kong or tell the people of Tonga how to make an austerity Christmas pudding from cabbage stumps and cream of tartar.*

## 4.7    Currency

**Decimalisation** has not yet been fully accepted in the Grunty Fen area; shops and individuals remain willing to accept or offer half crowns, shillings and pence. The traveller is wise to carry duodecimal as well as decimal currency when attempting to make a purchase in the more remote areas.

Setting conventional currency aside, **barter** is the main means of buying and selling. The market has its up and downs but broadly speaking a net of Brussels sprouts is worth a quart of paraffin and a net of carrots is worth 10 Woodbine cigarettes. Use these exchange rates only as guidelines in your dealings.

It is unlikely that a visitor merely passing through will become involved in hard currency deals involving railway sleepers although in the last analysis it is the extent of a local family's sleeper holdings that marks their real wealth and social status. However, visitors wishing to try the system may buy a starter pack of sleepers at the Post Office or Potts' Garage.

## 4.8   Cuisine

The culinary scene in Grunty Fen is simple yet generally quite nourishing but there are a few dishes for which it is widely known.

**Spam Fritters** may sound humdrum but when they are made with a can of the '43 or even the rare '44 Spam (of which a small supply may still be available), we have a dish of epicurean succulence. Lucky the visitor who – as a guest in some modest fen home – is offered this paradisal delicacy. Alas, supplies of both the 1944 and 1945 Spam are rapidly dwindling and those surviving cans are in such a critical condition that the least movement can cause those that have "blown" to explode. This makes searching remote World War II concrete pillboxes a risky business and finding a single can is fraught with danger. Like truffles, a can of the '43 or the '45 can fetch a huge price. Seven sleepers were paid for a can of the cheaper '45 at the time of Her Majesty's Jubilee but such transactions are seldom reported.

**Brawn Horns** are the speciality of Grunty Fen Women's Institute who are justly celebrated for their catering. Their brawn horns bring together two unique comestibles. Supplies of empty horns are obtained by the WI whenever the cream gun at the nearby patisserie bakery, "The Fancies," is left unattended on the night shift and breaks down. As a result the machinery produces great quantities of pastry horns while the cream is shot wide of them. On these occasions the ladies arrange for a truck load of pigs' heads to be shipped over from Poland and for two days the Village Hall is a scene of intense industry as the flensing and boiling processes are completed. The ladies believe this brawn will taste even better when they can arrange refrigerated transport for the heads.

Once it has set solid, scoops of the savoury jelly are inserted into the horns where the cream would have been if the gun had not gone wrong. The WI then sells this great delicacy to raise funds for Institute equipment. By this means they have already bought a complete angle grinder maintenance kit which they share to maintain their domestic angle grinders and reduce running costs.

**Road Kill Pie.** Like BLT elsewhere, the initials RKP are well known in Grunty Fen to signify one of the staple foods of the entire area, particularly those villages close to the A10.

In the misty light of dawn whatever the weather, whatever the season, you may see local people cycling or walking slowly along every road in search of the making of RKP.  Hares, pheasants, rabbits, partridges and even hedgehogs and owls which have been killed by passing traffic overnight are eagerly gathered for the pot.  Taken home these slightly squashed but generally complete little corpses are used by thrifty housewives to make the Road Kill Pie for which they are justly famous.  Try it, but be ready for a bit of grit!

### 4.8.1    Eating Out

**The Bull Inn** in Grunty Fen has an unpretentious menu yet offers filling fare for those who enjoy mushy pea sandwiches (hard to eat without squirting but you'll soon get the knack) or rabbit scratchings.

However, for those in search of fine dining, **The Gladlen** is an interesting experience.  Strangers often fail to find The Gladlen because this popular transport café looks at first like a tottering heap of pallets.  But once you have found a way through the pallets (watch out for the guard dogs!) you will be warmly welcomed by Gladys or Len whose scrupulous hygiene involves wiping down every table with Jeyes fluid after and sometimes during each meal.

Try the fried pork chops which Len proudly boasts "have a bit of kidney in every one."  Even better, try mink pasties made from fur-farm escapees. A note of caution: early diners at The Gladlen should avoid Gladys' mandarin jelly because all the fruit segments sink to the bottom of the bucket so only later diners get any fruit.

There is an official illustrated road map of the entire Grunty Fen area in full colour (cream and black) available from the Dennis of Grunty Fen website:

www.dennisofgruntyfen.co.uk.

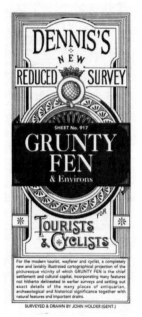

*This document - extracts of which are seen throughout this book - measures almost 2' by almost 1'6" and so "map" is too small a word for this lavishly illustrated cartographical projection incorporating many features hitherto not delineated in earlier surveys and setting out exact details of the many places of antiquarian, archaeological and historical significance together with natural features and important drains, surveyed and drawn by world-renowned artist Mr John Holder.*

# Further reading

*The Origin, Identification and Management of Mud*
(Grimwode et al, Geneva, 1931)

*The Role of the Rat in Entertainment and Navigation, a Brief History*
(Marigold Nettleford; privately published, 1989)

*'The Song of the Dyke', collected poems of Agatha Gotobed*
(Faerie Press, Dry Mincing, 1911)

*'A Miss is as Good as a Male', the story of Grunty Fen at War*
(Grunty Fen Women's Institute, 1990)

*'Don't Sit There!', The Carnivorous and Venomous Flora of Bleak Fen and District*
(Bunty Fordham, 1961)

*Some Handy Phrases in Rhubarb Semaphore*
(Denzil Runt, British Institute of Information Technology, 1938)

*How Stale Pastry Can Change Your Life*
(Madame Muriel Burke, privately published, 1972)

*The Book of Ezeriah*
(St Judas', Grunty Fen, one copy only)

# Further reading

*Repent, ye diabolical liars before judgment falls upon thee like an angry fox in the hen run of idle sinners for no mercy shall be shown unto they who squander their gifts in lust and fornication and suchlike*
(Rev S. Salmon, The Jonah's Press, 1980)

*How to Win at Bingo*
(Mrs Harriet Bismouth, 2 The Council Houses, Little Harm)

*'Galvanised!', The true story of Architectural Innovation in the Fens*
(Lecor Busier, Paris, 1951)

*Our Wonderful Fenland Holes*
(Anon., Ely, 1949)

*Vixens on Vespas – How I survived incarceration by the Little Sisters of Perpetual Availability*
(Nigel Smith, Concubine Press, 2002)

# Index

# Index

# Index

# Index

# Index

# Index

# Index

# Index

# Index

# Index

# Index

# Index